TABLE OF CONTENTS

* Full-color transparencies are found at the back of the book. Each transparency should be used to introduce the corresponding unit.

Teaching Guide

Page 1 ROCKETRY

CONCEPT: Rockets, using either solid or liquid propellants, are the vehicles that carry spacecrafts and satellites into space.

BACKGROUND INFORMATION: The age of rocketry perhaps had its beginning with the invention of crude gunpowder-rockets by ancient Chinese. Today scientists use rockets for space exploration and research. Rocket propellants (fuels) are either solid or liquid. Solid fuel rockets are more costly and complicated than the liquid fuel types. Solid fuel rockets burn a solid material called the grain, which consists of a fuel and an oxidizer in a solid form. The fuel, made up of dry chemicals, and the oxidizer (oxygen) are in one tank with a hollow core. The propellants burn from the core of the grain outward. Igniters start the fuels to burn. Liquid fuel rockets have two separate fuel tanks. One tank carries the fuel, either alcohol or refined kerosene, and one tank carries the oxidizer, liquid oxygen (LOX). The two fuels are pumped together and ignited. As in all rockets, the burning fuel produces hot, expanding exhaust gases that blast from the tail of the rocket and give a thrust forward. In order for a rocket to free itself from Earth's gravitational pull, it must reach an escape velocity of 40,000 kilometers per hour. Rockets are self-contained vehicles that follow Newton's Third Law of Motion which states, "for every action there is an equal and opposite reaction." Scientists have found that they can get rockets to travel faster and farther when they connect more than one rocket (stage) together. Each stage of the three-stage rocket has its own fuel and combustion chamber. The first stage, the largest, is located at the bottom and provides the initial thrust necessary to launch the spacecraft. After its fuel is used up, it drops off and the second stage is ignited, supplying the rocket with power. Eventually, the third stage remains to carry still farther the payload—spacecraft, men, or instruments.

ENRICHMENT ACTIVITIES: 1. Find out about the work of Robert H. Goddard and Wernher von Braun. 2. Find out about the differences between a jet engine and a rocket.

ANSWER KEY:
Page 1 1. nose cone — contains the "payload" —instruments, warheads, or man; fuel tanks — contain the propellants — liquid or solid fuel; rocket engine — contains the pump, combustion chambers, and exhaust nozzles 2. When the air-filled balloon is released, the balloon itself travels in one direction, and the escaping air travels in the opposite direction. **Study Question:** Scientists are developing a rocket that uses heat from nuclear reactors to change a liquid fuel into a gas. Such rockets can produce two or three times more power than solid or liquid fuel types.

Page 1a 1. A. action B. reaction 2. C. exhaust D. thrust 3. E. solid fuel rocket F. igniter — starts fuel burning G. fuel in solid fuel rocket H. combustion chamber I. exhaust nozzle J. liquid fuel rocket K. nose cone L. fuel tanks — liquid fuel M. pump N. combustion chamber 4. a. nose cone; instruments, warheads, or manned capsule b. alcohol, refined kerosene, liquid oxygen (LOX) c. blast; nozzle; speed 5. a. 5, thrust b. 2, payload c. 3, hinged rocket engine d. 1, solid fuel rocket e. 4, pump

Page 1b 1. vehicle assembly building 2. service structure (gantry) 3. camera stations 4. launch control center 5. umbilical tower 6. collects fuel overflow 7. a. 3 b. 2 c. 5 d. 4 e. 1

Page 2 EARLY SPACE PROJECTS

CONCEPT: Early space projects made important contributions in developing techniques and technology for future explorations of space by satellites.

BACKGROUND INFORMATION: When Russian scientists successfully launched the artificial satellite Sputnik in October 1957, the Space Age began. Following Sputnik, other types of satellites — communication, weather, navigation, and scientific — were successfully launched by Russian and American scientists. Soon thereafter animals and man were also traveling into space. Project Mercury was the first of three American space projects. The objectives of Project Mercury were to orbit a manned spacecraft, to investigate man's reaction to and abilities in space flight, and to recover both man and spacecraft safely. In April 1959, seven volunteers were chosen to participate in Project Mercury. These seven men became known throughout the world as America's first astronauts — Scott Carpenter, Gordon Cooper, John Glenn, Virgil Grissom, Walter Schirra, Alan Shepard, and Donald Slayton. Astronaut Shepard was the first American rocketed into space (May 1961) in manned spacecraft. His suborbital flight carried him 185 km high and 486 km away from the launch site, Cape Canaveral, Florida. He remained in space for ½ minutes. Astronaut Grissom duplicated Shepard's flight in July 1961. The first American to orbit Earth was astronaut John Glenn, Jr., in February 1962. He orbited Earth three times in less than five hours. Astronaut Carpenter duplicated Glenn's flight in May 1962. Project Mercury provided scientists sufficient data and techniques to undertake the next part of the American space program, Project Gemini. This project was to determine man's performance and behavior during prolonged space flight. The first pair of astronauts, Virgil Grissom and John Young, was orbited in a two-man spacecraft in March 1965. While orbiting Earth three times, they made changes in their orbital path, proving that man could "fly" a spacecraft in outer space. This led to another phase of Project Gemini — rendezvous and docking operations in space. The first rendezvous between two orbiting spacecraft was accomplished in March 1966 during the flight of Gemini 8 with astronauts Armstrong and Scott aboard. They were able to rendezvous and dock their spacecraft with another orbiting spacecraft, the Agena rocket. Many space flight endurance records were made and broken during Project Gemini. In June 1965, while a two-man spacecraft carrying astronauts McDivitt and White orbited Earth, astronaut White emerged from the spacecraft and became America's first astronaut to "walk" in space. This feat proved that man had the ability to leave the spacecraft, adjust, and leave the spacecraft, adjust, and perform certain operations in the environment of space. Project Gemini was truly an important "step into space" for man and his spacecraft.

ENRICHMENT ACTIVITIES: 1. Find out about passive and active satellites. 2. Find out how a spacecraft stays in orbit.

ANSWER KEY:
Page 2 1. Sputnik — first artificial satellite in space, marked the start of the Space Age; Project Mercury — gained experience in putting a man in orbit and recovering him successfully, studied the ability of man to function in the space environment; Project Gemini — studied man's reactions to long periods in space, ability to rendezvous and dock in space, and to function outside the spacecraft 2. From a relatively small and simple artificial satellite (Sputnik) launched in 1957 to the large, massive, complicated manned spacecrafts in Projects Mercury and Gemini launched from 1961 to 1966, a vast amount of scientific data and technology was gained in a few years. **Study Question:** Weightlessness or zero-g effects on man are still being evaluated — astronauts have lost weight, suffered from some disorientation, experienced a "lazy heart" and softening of their bones; acceleration — astronauts' weight increases seven or eight times that at Earth's surface; blood circulation, voluntary muscular activity, and visual acuity are affected; deceleration — vision is dimmed (double light intensity needed in reentry).

Page 2a 1. A. Sputnik I B. Project Mercury C. Project Gemini 2. D. first artificial satellite in space, marked start of Space Age E. first suborbital flight by an American, first American to orbit the Earth F. first to "fly" a spacecraft in space, first to rendezvous and dock in space, first American to "walk in space," first pair of Americans in space 3. a. Sputnik I; Russia; Space Age b. Project Gemini; orbits; fly c. Mercury; John Glenn; space or orbit 4. a. 2, E.H. White b. 4, Sputnik I c. 1, Agena d. 5, Project Mercury e. 3, Project Gemini 5. Project Gemini spacecraft were larger, heavier, and designed to stay in space for longer periods of time.

Page 3 THE SPACE ENVIRONMENT

CONCEPT: Space, where there is neither air nor gravity, is a hostile environment for man. Spacecrafts and space suits must provide ample protection for man if he is to survive in space.

BACKGROUND INFORMATION: After the advent of unmanned space flights, the man-in-space programs began. However, to put a man into space required solutions to new problems. The space environment can be a hostile one. There is no oxygen and no gravity, yet there are extreme temperature variations and deadly cosmic rays. Also, there is a danger of micrometeoroid bombardment. When astronauts work outside their spacecraft, they wear space suits which provide oxygen for breathing and provide for means to maintain proper air pressure and temperature. Since sound cannot travel through a vacuum, the space suit has an intercom radio system so the astronaut can communicate with fellow astronauts. A gauge on the arm of the space suit enables the spaceman to determine the exact air

pressure within the suit. The suit is flexible enough to allow free movement. There is a compact system for the removal of body wastes. Special pockets are located in easily accessible places for the storage of maps, instruction folders, data sheets, etc. The space suit is covered with a highly reflective material to help dissipate solar heat. On space shuttles, a thermal control system maintains comfortable temperatures within the shuttle and prevents problems that may result from exposure to intense heat or cold. The shuttles are designed to allow a "shirt-sleeve environment" so crew members have greater freedom and mobility within the craft. However, crew members wear a counter-pressure garment during reentry to help maintain normal blood circulation. With improvements in engineering and space medicine, there has been a great reduction in the hazards of living in the space environment.

ENRICHMENT ACTIVITIES: 1. Find out about astronaut selection and training. 2. Find out how astronauts maneuver during extra-vehicular activities.

ANSWER KEY:
Page 3 1. weightlessness, no air, hot and cold temperatures, radiation, intense sunlight, and micrometeoroid bombardment 2. The space suit is a portable life-support system that provides the astronaut with the essential needs for his survival. **Study Question:** Many layers of strong synthetic materials (nylon and Teflon) provide protection against micrometeoroids; highly reflective materials help dissipate solar heat; and a tinted face visor reduces the sun's glare.

Page 3a 1. weightlessness, no air, extreme hot and cold temperatures, radiation, intense sunlight, and micrometeoroid bombardment 2. A. portable life-support system B. communications carrier C. electrical power source D. pressure helmet E. tinted face visor F. backpack control box 3. disorientation, heart and skeletal difficulties 4. a. handholds, footholds b. space suit c. decompression, micrometeor 5. a. 4, cosmic and gamma rays b. 3, "lazy heart" c. 1, double walls d. 2, electrical system

Page 4 LUNAR EXPLORATION

CONCEPTS: 1. Project Apollo was the United States' mission to place astronaut-scientists on the surface of the moon and return them safely to Earth. 2. The project required detailed planning and precision in space maneuvering.

BACKGROUND INFORMATION: A Saturn V rocket launched the spacecrafts of Project Apollo on their destination to the moon. Information supplied by the Ranger, Surveyor, and Lunar Orbiter spacecrafts told of possible landing sites on and conditions of the lunar surface. Manned flights were conducted to study the maneuvering techniques required for the Apollo Project. The final step was the launching of the Apollo 11 on July 16, 1969, with the purpose of putting two astronauts on the moon. The spacecraft was first put into an Earth orbit. Then the command and service modules were turned around and docked with the third stage of the rocket vehicle. The rocket fired and thrust the spacecraft into lunar orbit. Two of the astronauts entered the lunar excursion module (LEM). The LEM detached itself and landed the two spacemen on the surface of the moon (July 20, 1969). The remaining astronaut stayed in the orbiting command and service module. On the moon, the astronauts made surveys of the moonscape features and collected rock samples. These tasks were not simple when one considers the lunar environment — reduced gravity, temperature extremes, no air, and solar glare. After completing their mission on the moon's surface, the astronauts reentered the lunar module. The ascent stage lifted off the moon's surface and allowed them to rendezvous and dock with the orbiting command and service module. The two astronauts transferred to the command-service module. The spacecraft was then made to turn around while in lunar orbit. Later the moon-landing module was separated and left behind. The spacecraft was then directed back toward Earth. En route to Earth, the service module was jettisoned, and the command module alone completed the journey back to Earth. The module was turned around to bring the heat shield to the front. Braking rockets were fired to slow its descent. Later, when the module was safely within Earth's atmosphere, the drag parachutes were opened, and the capsule slowly descended into the ocean.

ENRICHMENT ACTIVITIES: 1. Research the fictionalized accounts of moon travel by the writers Thomas D'Urfey and Jules Verne. 2. Find out about the estimated age of the moon.

ANSWER KEY:
Page 4 1. when the LEM is in orbit around the moon 2. braking rockets (not shown on illustration) and parachutes Study Question: Some findings include: the moon's surface is covered with a layer of fine dust; there are many meteor-impact craters; there is evidence of ancient volcanic activity; and there are moonquakes.

Page 4a 1. A. ascent stage B. descent stage 2. a. command module b. LEM c. service module 3. LEM must lift-off from the moon and dock with command module; these two units must fly to Earth; the service module separates from the command module which orbits Earth and lands in the ocean. 4. Saturn, Apollo 5. large, open areas free of large boulders 6. gravity, temperature, atmosphere

Page 4b 1. tracks of astronauts and Rover vehicle 2. electric; since there is no oxygen, combustion engines will not operate. 3. photographing, measuring surface features and atmospheric gases, spectroscopic analysis of radiation particles 4. to obtain core samples and for temperature experiments 5. The gravitational force is less; the package weighs less. 6. There is almost no atmosphere and no wind movements. (The flag was stiffened with a metal rod.)

Page 5 SPACE PROBES

CONCEPTS: 1. Space probes explore the solar system and space without subjecting astronauts to the dangers of space travel. 2. The probes contain a variety of sophisticated instruments to collect data.

BACKGROUND INFORMATION: American scientists have devised systematic space flight programs of unmanned space probes in order to save time, money, and human lives.

Space probes are sophisticated satellites, capable of collecting a variety of data from the moon, sun, and other planets. Some examples of unmanned space probes are the Ranger, Surveyor, Pioneer, Mariner, and Voyager. The Ranger project was started in 1959. Its purpose was to transport engineering and scientific instruments to the moon and to get high-resolution photographs of the lunar surface. There were many failures. Rangers 6 through 9 were most successful and relayed back to Earth more than 17,000 high-resolution pictures showing details of the lunar surface before they crashed, as scheduled, on the moon. A series of Mariner space probes flew to Venus and Mars and transmitted new information regarding the atmospheric and surface conditions of these two planets. Mariner 10, a 525-kg spacecraft, flew by Venus and then continued on toward Mercury, where it made two orbits around the planet coming from within 740 km of its surface. New and significant data was recorded for Venus and Mercury. The first of the Pioneer probes was launched in 1958 to study the Van Allen radiation belts. Pioneer probes 5 through 8 maneuvered through the solar system and relayed data about the sun and interplanetary space. Pioneer 10 achieved historical significance with the tremendous amount of data it transmitted before leaving the solar system in 1983.

ENRICHMENT ACTIVITIES: 1. Research the evidence that seems to indicate the presence of flowing water on Mars. 2. Find out about the conditions of Venus as discovered by early Pioneer and Mariner space probes.

ANSWER KEY:
Page 5 1. Pioneer 10 2. Mariner Study Question: Answers will vary.

Page 5a 1. A. meteoroid detector B. thruster C. magnetometer D. antenna E. solar panel F. solar panel G. antenna H. camera I. antenna 2. a. Mariner IX b. Pioneer 10 c. Mariner X d. Mariner IX e. Ranger f. Mariner II 3. a. provide electrical power b. film surfaces of planetary objects c. detect frequency of meteoroid bombardment d. maneuver spacecraft in flight e. receive and relay signals to and from Earth 4. Space probes can save time, money, and human lives.

Page 6 VIKING SPACE PROBE

CONCEPTS: 1. The Viking space probe carried instruments to the surface of Mars. 2. Soil was sampled, and tests for life were made.

BACKGROUND INFORMATION: The photographs from the Mariner 9 mission provided scientists information regarding where it was best to land Viking 1. On July 20, 1976, the Viking lander touched down on the surface of the red planet. Viking 2 landed on September 3, 1976. (The orbiter component has cameras and other instruments to select the landing sites.) When the lander was in orbit around Mars, it separated from the orbiter and descended to the planet's surface. A parachute helped slow its downward progress. After the lander came to rest on the surface of Mars, a variety of scientific instruments began to function to sample the atmosphere and surface. In addition to the meteorological, seismological, and imagery instruments, the landers had

Exploring Space

unique systems to determine if there was life on Mars. Mechanical arms scooped up soil samples which were conveyed to special chambers for testing to see if there were organisms which manufactured food, consumed food, or produced gases. It does not appear that there are organic compounds on the planet. The orbiter remained in orbit around the planet and took photographs of the surface. Many of the mysteries of the red planet were solved; many new questions were raised.

ENRICHMENT ACTIVITIES: 1. Research the specific activities performed by the Viking landers to determine if organic compounds were present on Mars. 2. Find out about the evidence of water on the surface of Mars.

ANSWER KEY:
Page 6 1. by the descent engine and the parachute 2. It continued to photograph the surface of Mars as it relayed the pictures to Earth. **Study Question:** Soil samples collected by the mechanical arm were conveyed into special sealed chambers. There, various biochemical tests were conducted to see if there were organic compounds which manufactured food, consumed nutrients, or produced gases as a result of metabolic activity.

Page 6a 1. A. camera B. antenna C. weather instrument D. earthquake detector E. descend engine F. collector head G. footpad 2. barren and rocky; very cold with a permafrost subsurface 3. A mechanical arm scooped material from the surface. 4. by the weather instruments recording data and transmitting it to Earth 5. a frozen subsoil 6. The volcano on Mars is about three times higher than Mount Everest, and the great canyon of Mars is about four times deeper and eight times wider than the Grand Canyon.

Page 7 VOYAGER SPACE PROBE

CONCEPTS: 1. The Voyager 1 and 2 space probes provided significant scientific data about the two giant planets. 2. Additional data about the distant planets of Uranus and Neptune is being gathered.

BACKGROUND INFORMATION: The space probes Voyager 1 and 2 were launched in 1977 and encountered Jupiter in 1979. Voyager 1 flew by Saturn in 1980, and Voyager 2 surveyed Saturn in 1981. The information relayed to Earth by these space probes about the giant planets was astonishing and unpredicted. Perhaps the most startling discovery was the finding of an active volcano on Jupiter's moon, Io. Computer-enhanced images of Io showed a large plume of sulfurous smoke rising 280 km from the surface. Also unsuspected was the thin ring found around Jupiter and the complexity of Saturn's rings. Both space probes transmitted data about the moons of these planets, including some newly discovered moons. The Voyagers have a variety of scientific instruments to study ultraviolet and infrared radiation, magnet fields, solar wind, charged particles, cosmic rays, zodiacal light, thermal energy, and meteoroid and cometary particles. Voyager 1 is en route to outer space. Voyager 2 is gathering data about Uranus and Neptune before continuing off into space.

ENRICHMENT ACTIVITIES: 1. Research the scientific data that was recorded by these Voyager instruments: radiation telescopes, imaging photopolarimeter, and scintillator. 2. Find out why Voyager 2 could not do a flyby of Pluto.

ANSWER KEY:
Page 7 1. It was not part of their mission, and the surfaces are gaseous. 2. the ultraviolet and infrared spectrometers **Study Question:** Answers may vary. Jupiter: Io — sulfur materials brought to surface by volcanoes; Europa — crust of ice; Ganymede — cratered surface on crust of ice; Callisto — many, many craters. Saturn: Titan — methane atmosphere; Enceladus — highly reflective surface of ice; Dione, Mimas, Rhea — all heavily cratered; Tethys — has very large trench across surface.

Page 7a 1. A. antenna B. magnetometer C. UV and IR spectrometers D. cameras E. generator 2. a. photographing planets and moons b. measuring magnetic fields around planets c. electric power supply 3. a. volcanoes b. has many rings c. has 16 moons d. Jupiter has rings. 4. to flyby and record information from Jupiter, Saturn, Uranus, and Neptune 5. meteoroid impacts and intense radiation

Page 8 SKYLAB

CONCEPTS: 1. Skylab was the first orbiting space station of the United States. 2. It was a scientific laboratory that provided data about Earth, the solar system, the universe, and the effects of weightlessness on people and materials.

BACKGROUND INFORMATION: On the afternoon of May 14, 1973, the United States launched Skylab from the Kennedy Space Center. It was the nation's first space station — an orbiting home, workshop, and laboratory for three astronauts. Skylab spacecraft consisted of five major components: 1) command and service module, 2) docking adapter, 3) solar observatory, 4) air lock, 5) workshop. The command and service module (CSM) functioned to bring the astronaut-scientists to the spacecraft and return them to Earth. The docking adapter not only contained the docking mechanism for the CSM, but also housed the controls for solar and Earth observation experiments. The solar observatory contained numerous instruments for the scientific study of the sun. In the air lock component of Skylab were the environmental, electrical, and communications control centers. The major module of Skylab was the workshop, which had a length of 14.6 m and a diameter of 6.70 m. There were approximately 295 cubic meters of work space. There were two compartments in the workshop. The lower level contained the crew's quarters for their daily living routine — eating, sleeping, and personal hygiene. Some experiments were also performed there. The upper level was the major scientific experimentation area. Much of the service equipment was stored in this level. Attached to the outside of the workshop was the solar array — two large panels of solar cells to help supply electricity for the spacecraft. The experiments and observations performed by the crews of Skylab missions provided valuable information about Earth's resources. It also gave detailed information about the sun and its activities, and about the life processes in space of humans and other organisms. An innovative feature of the Skylab program was the inclusion of experiments designed by high school students.

ENRICHMENT ACTIVITIES: 1. Research the effect of weightlessness on the circulatory system. 2. Find out about the kitchen and sleeping facilities aboard Skylab.

ANSWER KEY:
Page 8 1. solar panels 2. command module **Study Question:** The micrometeoroid detection shield, which also served as a heat and wind shield, was lost, and one of the solar panel arrays would not deploy. Emergency measures were taken to minimize the effect of solar radiation.

Page 8a 1. A. command and service module B. solar observatory C. docking adapter D. air lock E. workshop 2. a. crew's quarters b. command and service modules c. docking adapter d. science laboratory e. solar observatory f. science laboratory 3. People and materials float around if not fastened; no sense of up or down. 4. Astronauts would have to put on space suits and exit the Skylab to remove or replace film from the film compartment.

Page 8b 1. There would be no interference from the Earth's atmosphere (clouds, dust, etc). 2. a. locate areas for farming b. provide information about ocean currents c. locate potential areas where oil or minerals are likely to be found d. study movements and activities of storms 3. Crystals would be more perfect in shape and would be better conductors of electricity for use in special electronic apparatus. 4. appeared to be healthy and able to perform all activities; some lack of coordination in darkness 5. a. adjusted well and were able to spin regular webs b. grew somewhat erratic and did not exhibit usual response to light.

Page 9 THE SPACE SHUTTLE

CONCEPT: The space shuttle orbiter (SSO) is a reusable spacecraft designed to be launched like a rocket, to carry out a mission, and to land on Earth like an airplane.

BACKGROUND INFORMATION: The United States space program began to operate the space shuttle systems in the early 1980s. The space shuttle Orbiter (SSO) is the first reusable spacecraft, which greatly reduces the cost of space flights. In addition to reducing space flight costs, space shuttles can launch and repair satellites in space, send into deep space various types of probes, conduct experiments that require low or zero gravity, and in the future, build solar power stations and space communities. The space shuttle system consists of an orbiter, which is 37 meters (122 feet) long with a 24 meter (78 foot) delta-shaped wingspan; an external tank for liquid fuels; and two solid rocket boosters. Empty, the orbiter weighs about 68,000 kilograms (150,000 pounds). It can carry a crew of up to seven astronauts and 29,500 kilograms (65,000 pounds) of equipment. The liquid-fuel tank holds 703,000 kilograms (1,550,000 pounds) of propellant, liquid hydrogen, and liquid oxygen. This fuel tank is jettisoned prior to the space shuttle reaching orbit. The two recoverable solid rocket boosters assist the orbiter's three rocket engines at launch, each producing 375,000 pounds of thrust in overcoming Earth's gravitational pull. After two minutes in a space shuttle launch, the solid rocket boosters separate from the orbiter and return to Earth by parachute. They land in the ocean where, they are retrieved and made ready again for future use. After the shuttle completes its mission, the orbiter enters Earth's atmosphere and lands on a runway like an airplane. The first successful space shuttle flight took place in April 1981, when the "Columbia," with astronauts John Young and Robert Crippen in command, landed in the United States. The first American woman in space, Sally Ride, flew in the shuttle flight of "Challenger" in June 1983. The real value of the space shuttle program probably lies in the future. It will help in building large, complex space communities and solar power satellites; will carry advanced weather and communications satellites; and will produce new products like medicines, semiconductors, and optical materials. It will also be able to monitor Earth pollution problems, conduct wise management of resources and energy, assist in national security, and help make space a resource to be used for the good of mankind.

ENRICHMENT ACTIVITIES: 1. Find out about the European Space Research Organization (ESRO) and its space lab. 2. Find out about the Orbiter Processing Facility at the John F. Kennedy Space Center in Cape Canaveral, Florida.

ANSWER KEY:
Page 9 1. able to carry satellites, Skylabs, and a seven-man crew; build and maintain space stations; retrieve objects in space; place satellites into orbit; send data back to Earth; and return to Earth like an airplane 2. The shuttle system has reusable fuel tanks, and the orbiter itself can be used many, many times. **Study Question:** With a special propulsion system, space tugs will be able to move from one orbit to another, carrying space station modules to orbits around the moon. It will probably be able to send unmanned spacecrafts from an Earth orbit to an orbit around Mars.

Page 9a 1. A. speeding into space B. releasing Skylab into orbit C. using boon to "nab" an object in space D. traveling with doors open E. beaming information to Earth F. entering Earth's atmosphere 2. a. used b. rocket, airplane c. repair, return d. high or hot 3. a. 3, space shuttle b. 4, ceramic tiles c. 1, shuttle "arm" d. 2, Skylab or satellite 4. easier to launch satellites or space probes outside the gravitational pull of Earth

Page 9b 1. solid 2. 2 minutes 3. liquid 4. orbiter and two booster rockets, external fuel tank 5. It is 184 feet tall, and can carry 32½ tons into orbit. 6. five 7. a. 4, Columbia b. 1, three c. 5, Sally Ride d. 2, Challenger e. 3, Challenger flight of 1984 8. carrying materials, supplies, and persons to live and work in the space station, as well as bringing people and things back to Earth

Page 10 SPACE TECHNOLOGY BENEFITS

CONCEPT: The vast amount of research and advancement in space technology produced the necessities for space flights and "spin off" products that can be used in medicine, industry, and the home.

Exploring Space

BACKGROUND INFORMATION: Space medicine research has produced many well-known products aiding hospitals, doctors, and patients. These "spin-off" products include special glasses that sense eye movements and enable handicapped persons to operate wheelchairs and switches; tiny hearing aids that are inconspicuous; flexible tubing with light transmitting devices enabling doctors to actually see inside a patient's body; and a television camera the size of a box of cough drops mounted on the head of a surgeon enabling students a close-up view of an operation. The "new" field of biotelemetry — monitoring patients' temperature, heartbeat, and other vital components — has gained an abundance of benefits from space technology. Also, application of space technology has provided benefits to various industries. Perhaps the most notable and common benefit is microminiaturization. Large, bulky machines and computers can now be reduced to very small sizes and still function as well as or better than before reduction. Small tuning forks that vibrate 144 times as fast as the balance wheel in a watch are "spin off" products. Fiberglass materials that are lightweight and strong are used in storage tanks, railway tank cars, and truck tankers. Each day brings a new product or technique developed by space technology. In our homes, the "spin-off" is also noticeable. Some examples include an aluminized plastic blanket that can be folded and carried in a pocket, caulking material for tiles and other household uses (derived from sealants used in shuttles and other spacecraft), and the home computer parents and students can use for various tasks. In cookware, the material Teflon is a "spin-off" product.

ENRICHMENT ACTIVITIES: 1. Find out about the use of silicon chips in microminiaturization. 2. Find out about the management technique called the systems approach.

ANSWER KEY:
Page 10 1. Medical — tiny hearing aids; flexible tubing with light sensors enabling doctors to see inside the body; glasses that are sensitive to eye movement enabling handicapped persons to operate wheelchairs and switches; and biotelemetry. Industrial — microminiaturization, especially in computers and watches; lightweight fiber-glass material for storage and transporting purposes. Home — caulking compounds; home computers; aluminized, plastic blankets 2. Spacecrafts have a limited amount of space within the craft; size-reduction is a must and is improving with each new space project. **Study Question:** A plastic polymer gel with the density of human fat at body temperature is used as a padding for bedridden patients (to prevent bedsores), and enables burn victims to "float" on a cushion of air, speeding the healing process because the patients do not rub against bed clothes.

Page 10a 1. A. Medicine or medical, B. Industrial, C. Home 2. X—small segment of the computer; circle—patient attached by wires to a TV screen; box—home computer 3. hearing 4. sight or eyes 5. silicon chips 6. caulking compounds 7. a. 4, microminiaturization b. 1, fiberglass c. 2, biotelemetry d. 3, aluminized plastic 8. Often what can be used in one area can also be used with or without modifications in another area, such as microminiaturization used in medical, industrial, and home areas.

Page 11 SPACE COMMUNITIES

CONCEPT: In the not too distant future, scientists will be able to build colonies in space where various scientific activities can be performed by hundreds of people.

BACKGROUND INFORMATION: Using space shuttles, a modular space station could be established and then expanded to house hundreds of people. These people, "space colonists," would live and work in space for many months at a time. They would live in a huge, wheel-shaped structure that would rotate to create artificial gravity. To protect the colonists from hazardous cosmic radiation, an artificial shield made from lunar rock would encircle the wheel-like structure. A huge mirror placed above the wheel would reflect sunlight toward the colony for lighting and power purposes. Solar panels would also be used for power. Aboard the wheel, colonists would perform a variety of activities: manufacturing products in levels of low or zero gravity; doing biological research; making observations into space free from atmospheric interference; serving as a selection and training center for crews with long duration or deep space missions; and observing our planet. An interesting function of space communities is that scientists will be able to broadcast and televise summaries of their experiments directly into classrooms throughout the world. Some scientists state that these space communities will serve as orbital hospitals, hotels, and recreational facilities for space travelers. The essential living conditions within the community must be like that on Earth — air to breathe; water to drink and use; ways to eliminate wastes; means for exercise, sleep, and play. The ultimate goal of space scientists is to be able to do in space whatever is done on Earth.

ENRICHMENT ACTIVITIES: 1. Find out about the training methods used to accustom space travelers to weightlessness. 2. Find out about the unusual space community in the short novel, The Brick Moon, written by Everett Hale in 1869 and 1870.

ANSWER KEY:
Page 11 1. rotating "wheel" creates artificial gravity; mirror used to reflect sun rays for light and power; lunar rock shield for protection from cosmic rays; space stations for laboratories; space shuttles used for carrying supplies, materials, and personnel between Earth and space community. 2. Shuttles are the life lines for essential items and personnel living in the space community. **Study Question:** If spacecrafts are in trouble, or if persons are sick or injured in space, people can climb into large rescue balls and be carried to a space community hospital or rescue shuttle.

Page 11a 1. A. reflecting mirror B. community living quarters C. solar panels D. mechanical arm E. space shuttle F. space stations 2. d. air, water, exercise, sleep or rest 3. a. space shuttle b. moon, cosmic radiation c. sun d. oxygen and hydrogen e. exercise 4. a. 3 b. 4 c. 1 d. 2

Page 12 FUTURE IN SPACE EXPLORATION

CONCEPTS: 1. Space explorations of the future will depend on structures orbiting Earth. 2. Some of these structures are envisioned as being very large and must be assembled in space.

BACKGROUND INFORMATION: To escape the gravitational force of Earth, rockets must have tremendous thrust. Large amounts of fuel are consumed. This is very costly. Once in space, when the gravitational force is greatly reduced, the rocket fuel can be used much more efficiently. A space station with supplies of rockets would provide the opportunity to refit the spacecraft and allow it to travel farther into space. Super antennas orbiting in space can observe and record details of celestial objects that cannot be obtained from Earth-based instruments, which must penetrate the lights of cities and the haze and clouds of the atmosphere. These huge structures might be 100 meters in diameter. They can be delivered by space shuttles and either unfolded like an umbrella or erected from unassembled components. Another structure of the future will be solar power stations. These stations will collect solar radiation and transform it into electrical energy for use by various modules attached to a super structure. The modules may house a variety of scientific instruments and unmanned laboratories. Programmed robots may be used to fabricate structures or perform tasks too dangerous for people.

ENRICHMENT ACTIVITIES: 1. Research the benefits of producing pharmaceuticals in space. 2. Find out about some science fiction writers' concepts of space stations and exploration.

ANSWER KEY:
Page 12 1. Super antennas in space would be able to detect particles and signals from deep space without interference from Earth's atmosphere. 2. by space shuttles **Study Question:** freezing temperatures, radiation, and solar heat

Page 12a 1. A. super antenna B. solar power station 2. C. manipulator arm D. cargo bay 3. The super antenna would be folded compactly in the cargo bay of a shuttle and taken into space to be deployed. 4. The solar power station could serve as a generator of electrical power to operate large space orbiting laboratories, launch sites, etc. 5. Large space stations would allow the gathering of data without interference from the atmosphere of the Earth.

A Last Look — Part I

A. 1. Boon does not belong. It is an arm-like extension. Pressure helmet and backpack are parts of a space suit.
   2. Antenna does not belong. It relays signals to and from Earth. Alcohol and kerosene are liquid rocket fuels.
   3. Voyager does not belong. It is a space probe. Columbia and Challenger are space shuttles.
   4. Deafness does not belong. It is associated with the medical benefit of a hearing aid. Disorientation and heart difficulties are induced by weightlessness.
   5. Discovery does not belong. It is a shuttle mission. Viking and Mariner are space probes.
   6. Visor does not belong. It is part of a space suit. Igniter and core are parts of a solid fuel rocket.
   7. Decompression does not belong. It is a release of pressure caused by meteor bombardment.
   8. Nose cone does not belong. It is part of a rocket. Thrust and exhaust occur during take-off.
   9. Meteor bombardment does not belong. It is a hazard in the space environment. Stellar astronomy and materials processing are Skylab experiments.

10. Communications carrier does not belong. It is part of a space suit. Rover and Lunar Excursion Module are used for exploring the lunar surface.

B. 1. nose cone   6. Russia, 1957
   2. the moon   7. "walk" in space
   3. Solid   8. LEM
   4. Columbia   9. Mars
   5. action, reaction 10. Space Age

A Last Look — Part II

1. A. Ranger   7. A. Pioneer
   B. camera   B. magnetometer

2. A. Viking   8. A. community "wheel"
   B. lander   B. mirror

3. A. LEM   9. A. Viking lander
   B. ascent stage   B. descend engine

4. A. space shuttle 10. A. Sputnik I
   B. boon   B. antenna

5. A. Mariner   11. A. Gemini
   B. solar panel   B. Agena rocket

6. A. Voyager   12. A. space shuttles
   B. camera   B. solid fuel rockets

A Last Look — Part III

A. 1. g   B. 1. three
    2. h   2. boon
    3. a   3. ceramic tiles
    4. k   4. seven
    5. i   5. Traveler
    6. c   6. John Glenn
    7. d   7. five
    8. l   8. kerosene
    9. f   9. helmet
   10. j   10. docking

A Last Look — Part IV

A. The members of the space shuttle are alluding to the fact that space travel is becoming more common.

B. 1. The arrow is pointing to the rocket, not the shuttle.

    2. The shuttle lifts-off in an upright position from a launch pad with the aid of rockets. It does not take off like a plane.

    3. The arrow is pointing to the boon, not the antenna.

    4. The shuttle lands like a plane, so the parachute is unncessary.

C. I will beam you up after you get my cheeseburgers and fries. Scotty.

                        Exploring Space

The following section contains the student worksheets. Each worksheet should be introduced by the corresponding transparency found at the back of this book.

Rocketry

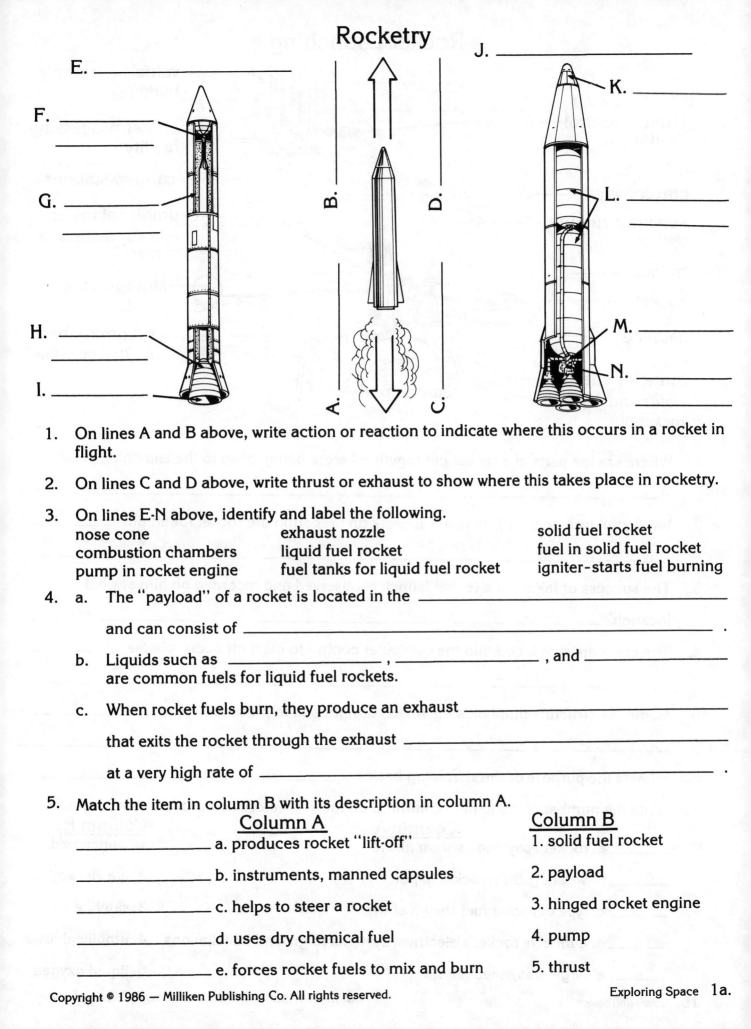

E. _____

F. _____
   _____

G. _____
   _____

H. _____
   _____

I. _____

B.   D.

A.   C.

J. _____

K. _____

L. _____
   _____

M. _____

N. _____
   _____

1. On lines A and B above, write action or reaction to indicate where this occurs in a rocket in flight.

2. On lines C and D above, write thrust or exhaust to show where this takes place in rocketry.

3. On lines E-N above, identify and label the following.
   nose cone   exhaust nozzle   solid fuel rocket
   combustion chambers   liquid fuel rocket   fuel in solid fuel rocket
   pump in rocket engine   fuel tanks for liquid fuel rocket   igniter-starts fuel burning

4. a. The "payload" of a rocket is located in the _____

      and can consist of _____ .

   b. Liquids such as _____ , _____ , and _____
      are common fuels for liquid fuel rockets.

   c. When rocket fuels burn, they produce an exhaust _____

      that exits the rocket through the exhaust _____

      at a very high rate of _____ .

5. Match the item in column B with its description in column A.
   ### Column A
   _____ a. produces rocket "lift-off"

   _____ b. instruments, manned capsules

   _____ c. helps to steer a rocket

   _____ d. uses dry chemical fuel

   _____ e. forces rocket fuels to mix and burn

   ### Column B
   1. solid fuel rocket

   2. payload

   3. hinged rocket engine

   4. pump

   5. thrust

Rocket Launching

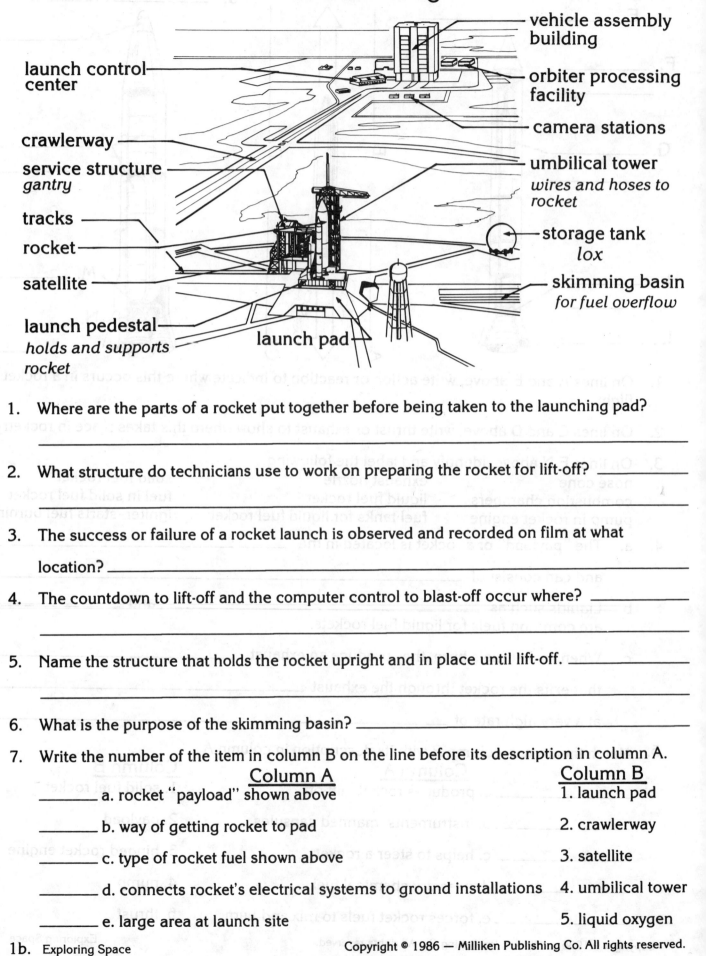

launch control center

crawlerway

service structure
gantry

tracks

rocket

satellite

launch pedestal
holds and supports rocket

launch pad

vehicle assembly building

orbiter processing facility

camera stations

umbilical tower
wires and hoses to rocket

storage tank
lox

skimming basin
for fuel overflow

1. Where are the parts of a rocket put together before being taken to the launching pad?

_____

2. What structure do technicians use to work on preparing the rocket for lift-off? _____

3. The success or failure of a rocket launch is observed and recorded on film at what

   location? _____

4. The countdown to lift-off and the computer control to blast-off occur where? _____

_____

5. Name the structure that holds the rocket upright and in place until lift-off. _____

_____

6. What is the purpose of the skimming basin? _____

7. Write the number of the item in column B on the line before its description in column A.

<u>Column A</u>

_____ a. rocket "payload" shown above

_____ b. way of getting rocket to pad

_____ c. type of rocket fuel shown above

_____ d. connects rocket's electrical systems to ground installations

_____ e. large area at launch site

<u>Column B</u>

1. launch pad

2. crawlerway

3. satellite

4. umbilical tower

5. liquid oxygen

Early Space Projects

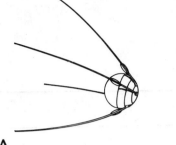

A. _____   B. _____   C. _____

D. _____   E. _____   F. _____

_____   _____   _____

1. On lines A, B, and C above, identify and label the following.

    Project Gemini   Sputnik I   Project Mercury

2. On lines D–F above, write two accomplishments of each early space project.

3. a. The first artificial satellite in space was called _____ ,

    launched in the country of _____ and is said to have started the

    _____ _____ .

   b. When the two-man spacecraft in _____ _____

    was able to change its _____ , it proved that the United

    States had a spacecraft that man could " _____ " in space.

   c. The first flight in Project _____ was a suborbital flight,

    but the second flight did put the American astronaut _____

    _____ into _____ .

4. Match the name in column B with its description in column A.

    <u>Column A</u>   <u>Column B</u>

    _____ a. went for a "walk" in space   1. Agena

    _____ b. "traveler" of a foreign country   2. E.H. White

    _____ c. target for rendezvous and docking   3. Project Gemini

    _____ d. first Americans in space   4. Sputnik

    _____ e. proved man could stay in space for a long time 5. Project Mercury

5. The launch vehicles (rockets) in Project Gemini were larger and had more thrust than

    those in Project Mercury. Why? _____

    _____

The Space Environment

A. _____

B. _____

C. _____

D. _____

E. _____

F. _____

1. List four factors found in the space environment._____

_____

2. On lines A- F above, identify and label the parts of a space suit.

   electrical power source   pressure helmet   communications carrier

   portable life-support system   tinted face visor   backpack control box

3. What are two common problems astronauts might experience in a prolonged weightless

   environment?_____

4. a. In order for an astronaut to work in a weightless environment, _____

   and _____ are needed to provide anchorage.

   b. A portable life-support system is built into the _____ of
      an astronaut.

   c. The sudden loss of pressure called _____ in a spacecraft or

   space suit may result from _____ bombardment.

5. Match the item in column B with its description in column A.

Column A	Column B
_____ a. form of radiation in space	1. double walls
_____ b. a problem of weightlessness	2. electrical system
_____ c. spacecraft protection from meteors	3. "lazy heart"
_____ d. power source in a space suit	4. cosmic rays and gamma rays

3a. Exploring Space

Lunar Exploration

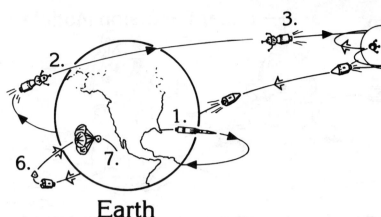

Moon

Earth

The Apollo Trips

1. Saturn rocket launches lunar spacecraft.
2. Command and service modules turn around and dock with third stage.
3. Mooncraft slows down and enters a moon orbit; astronauts enter lunar excursion module (LEM).
4. Lunar excursion module lands on moon; docks with command module.
5. Excursion module lifts off moon; docks with command module.
6. Service module separates from command module.
7. Command module lands in ocean.

A. _____

_____

B. _____

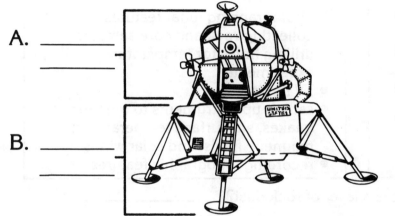

1. On lines A and B, identify and label the parts of the lunar spacecraft.
2. Name the spacecraft part involved in each of these lunar exploration activities.

   a. reenters Earth's atmosphere _____

   b. lands on lunar surface _____

   c. separates from command module before return to Earth _____

3. What maneuvers must be performed to return to Earth from the surface of the moon?

   _____

   _____

4. The _____ rocket launched the _____ spacecraft on its journey to the moon.

5. Describe the kind of lunar surface chosen to land the spacecraft. _____

   _____

6. List three environmental conditions on the moon's surface that had to be considered for

   Project Apollo. _____

   _____

Exploring the Lunar Surface

Command Module — Lunar Excursion Module

Rover

Activities in the Orbiting Command-Service Module

- photographing lunar surface
- measuring lunar features
- measuring lunar atmospheric gases
- spectroscopic analysis of radiation particles

Activities on the Lunar Surface

- photographing lunar features
- collecting rock and core samples
- drilling holes for temperature experiments
- TV filming
- setting up instruments to monitor quakes, subsurface temperatures, magnetic fields, and solar winds
- recording topographic features

1. What is the evidence that the moon has a layer of rock dust? _____

_____

2. What kind of motor did the Lunar Rover have? _____

   How do you know? _____

_____

3. List three research projects the astronaut did in orbit around the moon. _____

_____

4. Why did the astronaut drill holes into the surface of the moon? _____

_____

5. Why could an astronaut easily carry a package of instruments weighing nearly 140

   kilograms? _____

_____

6. Some photographs taken on the moon by astronauts show a flag that appears to be waving

   in the breeze. Why is this not possible? _____

_____

Space Probes

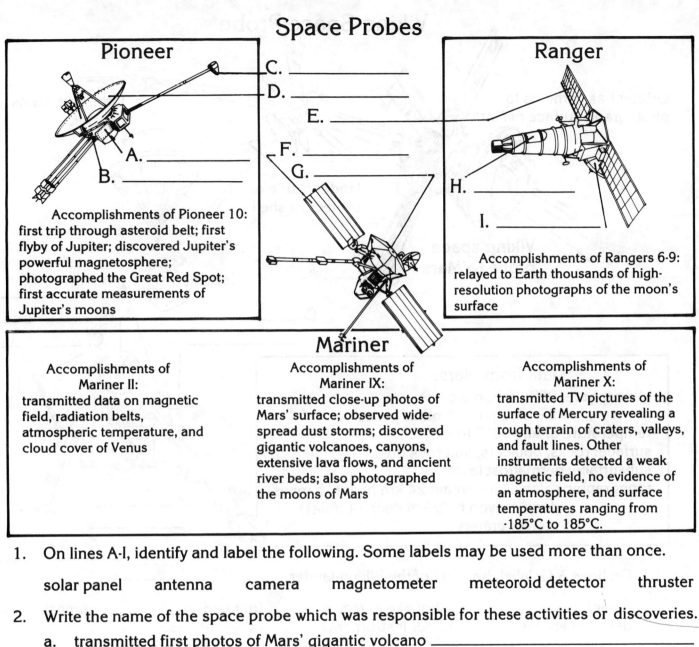

Pioneer

C. _____
D. _____
E. _____
F. _____
G. _____
A. _____
B. _____

Accomplishments of Pioneer 10: first trip through asteroid belt; first flyby of Jupiter; discovered Jupiter's powerful magnetosphere; photographed the Great Red Spot; first accurate measurements of Jupiter's moons

Ranger

H. _____
I. _____

Accomplishments of Rangers 6-9: relayed to Earth thousands of high-resolution photographs of the moon's surface

Mariner

Accomplishments of Mariner II: transmitted data on magnetic field, radiation belts, atmospheric temperature, and cloud cover of Venus

Accomplishments of Mariner IX: transmitted close-up photos of Mars' surface; observed widespread dust storms; discovered gigantic volcanoes, canyons, extensive lava flows, and ancient river beds; also photographed the moons of Mars

Accomplishments of Mariner X: transmitted TV pictures of the surface of Mercury revealing a rough terrain of craters, valleys, and fault lines. Other instruments detected a weak magnetic field, no evidence of an atmosphere, and surface temperatures ranging from -185°C to 185°C.

1. On lines A-I, identify and label the following. Some labels may be used more than once.

    solar panel   antenna   camera   magnetometer   meteoroid detector   thruster

2. Write the name of the space probe which was responsible for these activities or discoveries.
    a. transmitted first photos of Mars' gigantic volcano _____
    b. first flyby of the planet Jupiter _____
    c. revealed the moon-like surface of Mercury _____
    d. provided data for Viking landing on Mars _____
    e. crash-landed on moon after photographing surface _____
    f. transmitted data of Venus' thick cloud cover _____

3. What are the functions of these space probe instruments?
    a. solar panels _____   d. thrusters _____
    b. TV cameras _____   e. antenna _____
    c. meteoroid detector panels _____

4. Discuss the value of unmanned space probes for space exploration.

Exploring Space **5a.**

Viking Space Probe

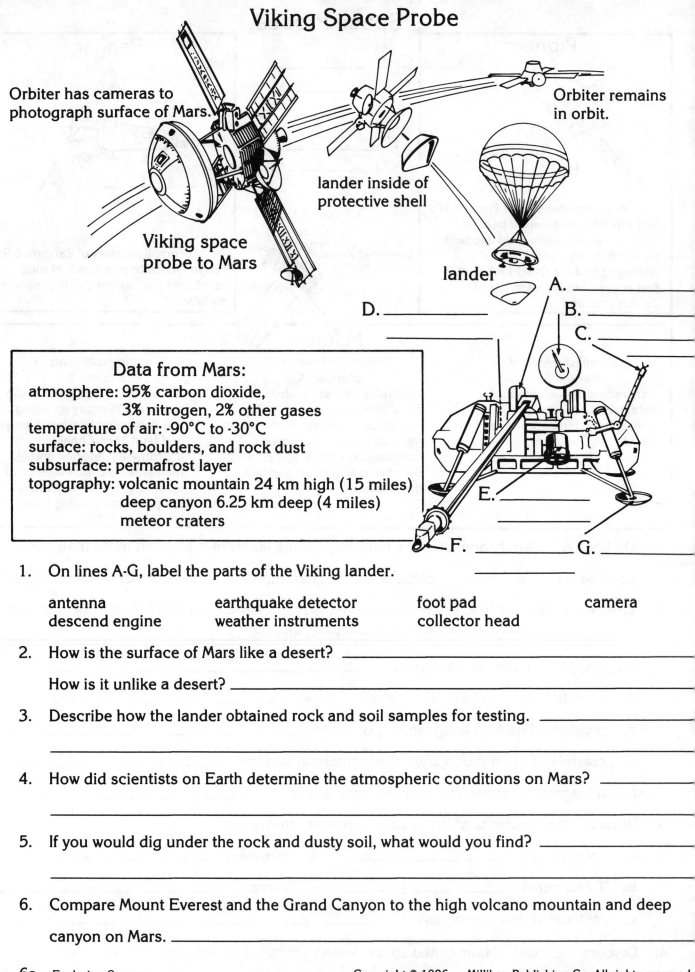

Orbiter has cameras to photograph surface of Mars.

Viking space probe to Mars

lander inside of protective shell

Orbiter remains in orbit.

lander

A. _____

B. _____

C. _____

D. _____

_____

E. _____

F. _____

G. _____

Data from Mars:
atmosphere: 95% carbon dioxide,
    3% nitrogen, 2% other gases
temperature of air: -90°C to -30°C
surface: rocks, boulders, and rock dust
subsurface: permafrost layer
topography: volcanic mountain 24 km high (15 miles)
      deep canyon 6.25 km deep (4 miles)
      meteor craters

1. On lines A-G, label the parts of the Viking lander.

    _____

| antenna | earthquake detector | foot pad | camera |
| descend engine | weather instruments | collector head | |

2. How is the surface of Mars like a desert? _____

   How is it unlike a desert? _____

3. Describe how the lander obtained rock and soil samples for testing. _____

   _____

4. How did scientists on Earth determine the atmospheric conditions on Mars? _____

   _____

5. If you would dig under the rock and dusty soil, what would you find? _____

   _____

6. Compare Mount Everest and the Grand Canyon to the high volcano mountain and deep

   canyon on Mars. _____

Voyager Space Probe

Mission: to flyby the planets Jupiter, Saturn, Uranus, and Neptune

A. _____

B. _____

C. _____

_____

_____

D. _____

E. _____

New Data from Voyagers 1 & 2
(1979 - 1981)

Saturn

ring composed of numerous bands; strong surface winds; has 17 moons; moon Titan has liquid methane on surface; moon Enceladus has a highly reflective surface of ice

Jupiter

has a thin ring; Great Red Spot releases heat from interior; has 16 moons; moon Ganymede has a crust of frozen water; moon Io has active volcanoes

1. On lines A-E, identify and label the parts of the Voyager space probe.
    ultraviolet and infrared spectrometers   magnetometer
    cameras   generator   antenna for communicating with Earth

2. Briefly describe the function of these components.

    a. camera _____

    b. magnetometer _____

    c. generator _____

3. Describe the discoveries made by the Voyager missions that prove these "facts" untrue.

    a. The moons of planets are geologically inactive. _____

    b. Saturn has three rings. _____

    c. Jupiter has eleven moons. _____

    d. Saturn is the only planet with a ring. _____

4. What is the total mission of the Voyager space probe? _____

    _____

5. What hazards can space probes encounter in flight? _____

    _____

Skylab

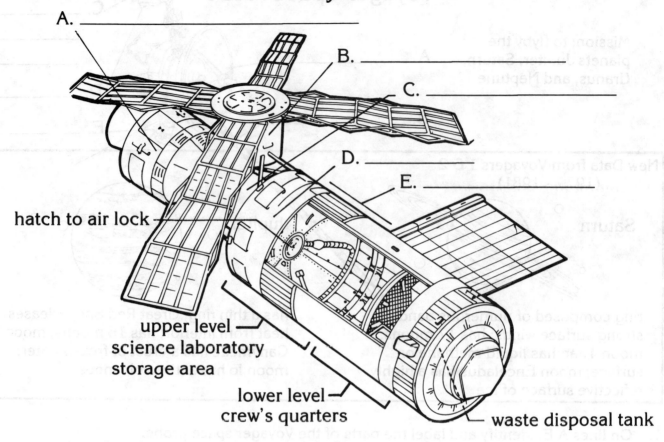

A. _____

B. _____

C. _____

D. _____

E. _____

hatch to air lock

upper level —
science laboratory
storage area

lower level —
crew's quarters

waste disposal tank

1. On lines A-E, identify and label the major components of Skylab.

solar observatory	workshop	air lock
docking adapter	command and service module	

2. With which Skylab component are these activities associated?

   a. meals _____

   b. leaving and returning to Earth _____

   c. coupling of command and service module to Skylab _____

   d. experiments designed by students _____

   e. observations of solar flares _____

   f. crystal growth experiment _____

3. What kinds of problems can weightlessness cause for the astronauts? _____

   _____

4. The film for the solar observatory can only be replaced and removed from the outside. How

   would the astronauts be able to perform this activity in space? _____

   _____

Skylab Experiments

Solar Observations

Revealed these discoveries: many short-term events occur in the corona; new details of photosphere; presence of "holes" in the corona which might be sources of solar winds; new features at the solar poles

Earth Resources Program

Analysis of photographs revealed: potential new energy sources in remote areas; new data on development of tropical storms; new data on ocean currents; more precise geographical location of Earth features

Medical Experiments

Revealed these responses to zero-gravity: astronauts could function effectively; had little motion sickness; some difficulty with coordinated hand movements in darkness; need for regular exercise

Student Experiments

Web spinning by spider showed adaptation to weightlessness; some bacteria colonies grew more rapidly and had irregular shapes; rice seedling growth did not show usual response to light; rate of neutron flow was higher than expected.

Materials Processing

New processing techniques in zero-gravity produced: high-quality crystals; crystals with improved electrical conductivity; new alloys; crystals formed from vapors

Stellar Astronomy

New knowledge gained: ultraviolet magnitude of certain stars; X-ray spectra of stars

1. Why would observations of the sun and the stars be better from space than from Earth?

   _____

2. How could photographs from space aid the following?

   a. agriculture _____

   b. navigation _____

   c. prospecting for oil or minerals _____

   d. weather prediction _____

3. Why might it be useful to grow crystals in a space station for use on Earth? _____

   _____

4. Describe the general health and fitness of Skylab astronauts after several weeks of

   weightlessness. _____

5. How did these organisms respond to zero-gravity?

   a. spiders _____

   b. rice plant seedlings _____

The Space Shuttle

A. _____

B. _____

C. _____

F. _____

D. _____
    _____

E. _____

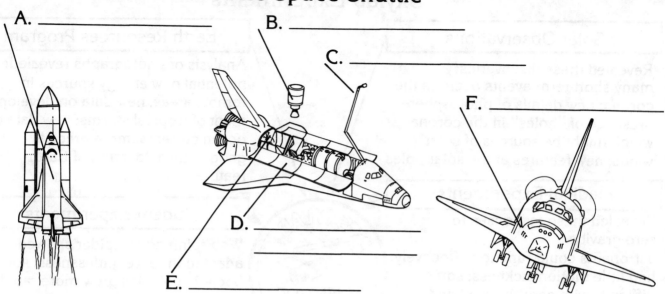

1. On lines A-F above, identify and label the following space shuttle activities.

   using a boon to "nab" an object in space   speeding into space

   releasing a skylab into orbit   beaming information to Earth

   traveling in space with cargo doors open   entering the Earth's atmosphere
   with a full cargo

2. a. A benefit of the space shuttle is that it can be _____ again and again.

   b. The space shuttle gets into orbit like a _____ ,

      but returns to Earth as an _____ .

   c. A space shuttle can "nab" a satellite and either _____

      it and send it back into orbit or _____ to Earth.

   d. When entering the Earth's atmosphere, shuttle crew members need protection from

      very _____ temperatures.

3. Match the item in column B with its name in column A.

Column A	Column B
_____ a. orbiter	1. shuttle "arm"
_____ b. heat shield	2. skylab or satellite
_____ c. boon	3. space shuttle
_____ d. payload	4. ceramic tiles

4. Why can the space shuttle system provide good exploration into deep space?_____

   _____

Space Shuttle Launching and Flights

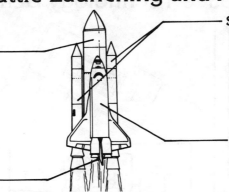

solid fuel booster rockets
used in lift-off;
released after two
minutes in flight;
rockets are reusable;
land in ocean

external fuel tank
liquid fuel
released just before
going into orbit;
tank not reusable;
"burn-up" in space

shuttle *orbiter*
carries flight crew,
mission specialists,
cargo; can be used
over 100 times

three main engines
used in lift-off

**space shuttle system
56.1 m (184 ft.) tall**

can carry a crew of seven; can carry 29,500 kg (32½ tons) into orbit; can put
satellites in orbit; repair and retrieve them; may carry people and supplies to and
from orbiting space stations; may launch space probes into deep space

Flights

- first successful space shuttle, April 1981, the United States "Columbia";
  astronauts John W. Young and Robert L. Crippen
- second flight of shuttle "Challenger," June 1983; first American woman in space,
  Sally Ride
- flight of shuttle "Challenger," February 1984; two crewmen made untethered
  space "walks" using propulsion backpacks
- "Discovery" and "Atlantis," space shuttle flights in 1980s

1. What type of fuel do booster rockets use to launch a space shuttle? _____

2. For how long do these rockets provide thrust during a launch? _____

3. What kind of fuel does the shuttle use as it nears orbit? _____

4. Name three reusable parts of a space shuttle system. _____

   _____

5. What two facts about the space shuttle indicate it is a big and powerful craft? _____

   _____

6. How many engines are used in sending the space shuttle off the launching pad? _____

7. Match the word or phrase in column B with its description in column A.

Column A	Column B
_____ a. number one U.S. space shuttle	1. three
_____ b. main engines on a shuttle	2. Challenger
_____ c. first U.S. female astronaut in space	3. Challenger flight of 1984
_____ d. second U.S. space shuttle	4. Columbia
_____ e. first nonconnected "walk" in space	5. Sally Ride

Space Technology Benefits

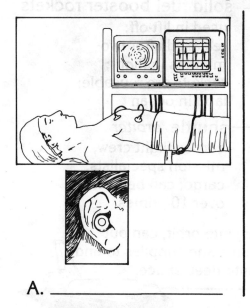  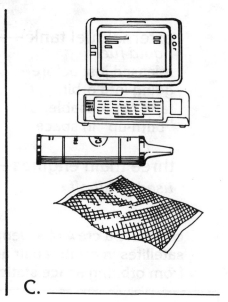

A. _____ B. _____ C. _____

1. On lines A, B, and C above, identify and label the areas in which space technology has provided benefits.

2. Identify the pictures above according to the following instructions.

    a. Put an X on a silicon chip that is greatly magnified.

    b. Put a circle around viewing a patient's internal organ.

    c. Put a box around something you might use to do homework.

3. Which sense of a handicapped person has been aided by space technology? _____

4. Persons confined to wheelchairs can now use which sense for some mobility? _____

5. Where are complex circuits located in modern high-speed microcomputers? _____

6. Which space technology benefit can builders use to seal windows and doors? _____

7. Match the item in column B with its description in column A.

Column A	Column B
_____ a. great reduction in size of computers	1. fiberglass
_____ b. strong, lightweight storage material	2. biotelemetry
_____ c. monitoring systems in hospitals	3. aluminized plastic
_____ d. space-age blanket material	4. microminiaturization

8. Why do space technology benefits often affect more than one area of our lives? (Give an example from the pictures above.) _____

    _____

    _____

Space Communities

A. _____

B. _____

_____

C. _____

D. _____

E. _____

F. _____

1. On lines A-F, identify and label the following.

   space shuttle   mechanical arm   community living quarters

   reflecting mirror   space stations   solar panels

2. List four earth-like needs of persons living in space. _____

   _____

3. a. The carrier of supplies, materials, and persons to space communities is the

   _____ _____ .

   b. Rocks from the _____ will provide space communities

   protection from _____ _____ .

   c. A natural source of reflected light and energy is provided by the _____ .

   d. Air to breathe must contain the gases _____ and _____ .

   e. Because the heart and muscles work less in weightlessness, _____
   is vital in space living.

4. Write the number of the item in column B on the line before its description in column A.

Column A	Column B
_____ a. cards, checkers, dominoes	1. space shuttle
_____ b. constant "wheel" rotation	2. community "wheel"
_____ c. "link" between Earth and space community	3. space community recreation
_____ d. where colonists live, work, and play	4. artificial gravity produced

Future in Space Exploration

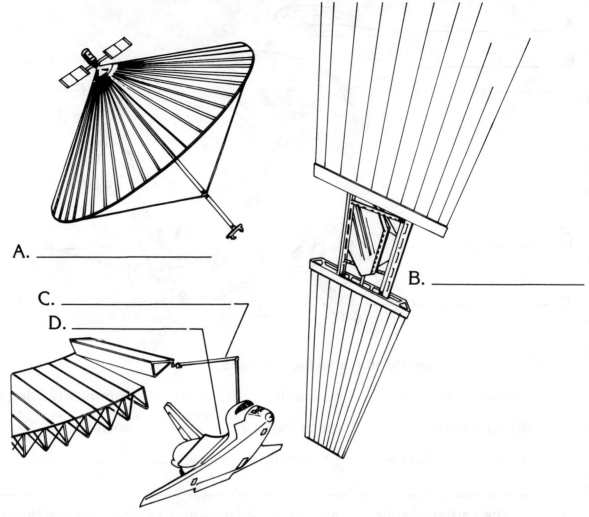

A. _____

B. _____

C. _____

D. _____

1. Label the space structures being considered for future space use and exploration.

   super antenna   solar power station

2. Label the parts of the space shuttle.

   cargo bay   manipulator arm

3. Describe how the umbrella-like super antenna can be transported into space in the

   relatively small cargo bay of the space shuttle. _____

   _____

4. What might be the value of a space solar power station orbiting around Earth?_____

   _____

   _____

5. Briefly describe the value of a space station to the study of outer space. _____

   _____

   _____

12a. Exploring Space

A Last Look — Part I

A. In each of the following groups, one item does not belong. Circle that item and in the space provided explain why it does not belong.

1. pressure helmet   backpack   boon
_____

2. alcohol   antenna   kerosene
_____

3. Voyager   Columbia   Challenger
_____

4. disorientation   heart difficulties   deafness
_____

5. Viking   Discovery   Mariner
_____

6. igniter   visor   core
_____

7. biotelemetry   microminiaturization   decompression
_____

8. nose cone   thrust   exhaust
_____

9. stellar astronomy   materials processing   meteor bombardment
_____

10. Rover   Communications Carrier   Lunar Excursion Module
_____

B. Write the word or words that will make each sentence a true statement.

1. The "payload" is carried in the _____ of a rocket.

2. Ranger crash-landed on _____ after photographing its surface.

3. _____ fuel burns from the core outward.

4. _____ was the first successful space shuttle.

5. The Third Law of Motion states that for every _____ there is

   an equal and opposite _____ .

6. The first artificial satellite in space was launched by _____

   in the year _____ .

7. In June 1965, E. H. White became the first American to _____ .

8. The _____ is the part of a spacecraft that lands on the lunar surface.

9. The Viking space probe studied the planet _____ .

10. The launch of Sputnik I marked the start of the _____ .

A Last Look — Part II

On line **A**, name the spacecraft indicated.

On line **B**, label the part of the spacecraft indicated.

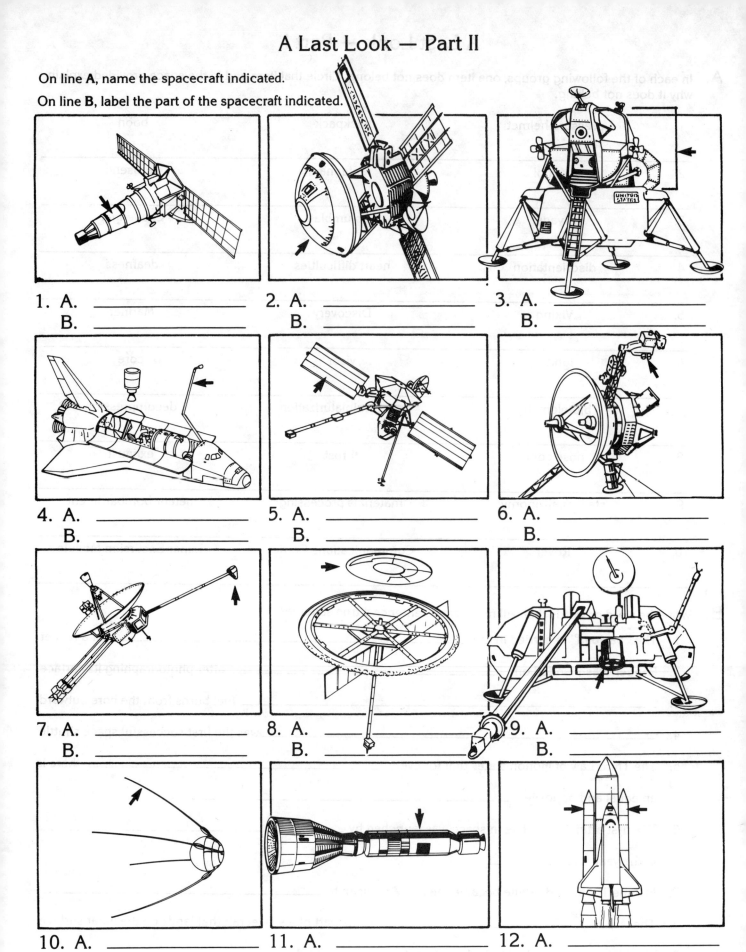

1. A. _____
   B. _____

2. A. _____
   B. _____

3. A. _____
   B. _____

4. A. _____
   B. _____

5. A. _____
   B. _____

6. A. _____
   B. _____

7. A. _____
   B. _____

8. A. _____
   B. _____

9. A. _____
   B. _____

10. A. _____
    B. _____

11. A. _____
    B. _____

12. A. _____
    B. _____

A Last Look — Part III

A. Find the statement in the second column that best describes each word or phrase in the first column. Write the letter of the statement before the word it describes.

1. _____ Pioneer
2. _____ E. H. White
3. _____ Jupiter
4. _____ launch pad
5. _____ thrust
6. _____ Mariner
7. _____ John Glenn
8. _____ rockets
9. _____ LEM
10. _____ Saturn

a. has 16 moons
b. part of a space suit
c. flyby missions to Mercury, Venus, and Mars
d. first American in orbit
e. arm-like extension on spacecraft
f. lands on lunar surface
g. flyby missions to Jupiter and Saturn
h. first American to "walk" in space
i. produces rocket "lift off"
j. has a ring with numerous bands
k. concrete structure from which rocket is launched
l. vehicles that carry satellites into space

B. Circle the word or phrase that will make each sentence a true statement.

1. Rockets have _____ main parts.

   two   three   four

2. A _____ is an arm-like extension used to retrieve objects in space.

   boon   thruster   propellant

3. The heat shield of the space shuttle is made of _____ .

   asbestos pads   plastic cups   ceramic tiles

4. The space shuttle can carry a crew of _____ .

   seven   nine   eleven

5. _____ was the first artificial satellite.

   Mercury   Traveler   Viking

6. The first American in orbit was _____ .

   John Glenn   Alan Shepard   E. H. White

7. The space shuttle uses _____ engines to launch.

   five   ten   fifteen

8. A common liquid fuel for rockets is _____ .

   gasoline   propane   kerosene

9. The intercom-radio system is contained in the _____ of an astronaut's space suit.

   belt   helmet   backpack

10. The joining of spacecrafts in space is called _____ .

   reentry   docking   orbiting

A Last Look — Part IV

A. Explain fully the meaning of this cartoon.

_____

_____

_____

_____

B. There is something wrong with each of these drawings. Circle the part of the picture that is incorrect and explain why you circled it.

shuttle.

1. _____

"lift off" from launch pad

2. _____

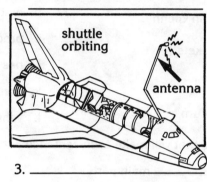

shuttle orbiting

antenna

3. _____
_____

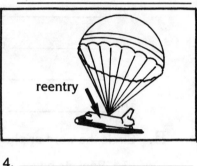

reentry

4. _____
_____

C. Use the following position code to decode the message received from outer space.

TRANSPARENCY SECTION

(Use the transparencies to introduce each lesson.)